I HERO

BLOOD CROWN QUEST
CITY OF THE DEAD

Steve Barlow and Steve Skidmore
Illustrated by Jack Lawrence

First published in 2013
by Franklin Watts

Text © Steve Barlow and Steve Skidmore 2013
Illustrations by Jack Lawrence © Franklin Watts 2013
Cover design by Jonathan Hair

Franklin Watts
338 Euston Road
London NW1 3BH

Franklin Watts Australia
Level 17/207 Kent Street
Sydney, NSW 2000

A CIP catalogue record for this book
is available from the British Library.

(ebook) ISBN: 978 1 4451 1506 1
(pb) ISBN: 978 1 4451 1502 3
(Library ebook) ISBN: 978 1 4451 2524 4

1 3 5 7 9 10 8 6 4 2

Printed and bound by
CPI Group (UK) Ltd, Croydon, CR0 4YY

Franklin Watts is a division of Hachette Children's Books,
an Hachette UK company.
www.hachette.co.uk

3

You grip your sword tightly and rush forward. Your blade slices into one of the creatures and it drops to the floor.

But at the same moment the other two creatures transform into giants!

You are helpless as one of the giants grabs you and holds you upside down. The leather pouch containing the other rubies falls to the ground out of your reach.

The creature smashes you against the wall. He and his companion howl in glee as you pass out.

Go to 42.

4

Before the undead can attack, you hold up your hand. "Lay down your weapons!" you command. They immediately obey you.

Even the Red Queen is unable to act against the combined power of the rubies. You walk over to the crown, put the rubies into their settings, and place it on your head. You feel your soul returning to your body!

You face the Red Queen. "Begone forever!" you order. She bursts into flames and melts before your eyes.

You turn to Olderon. "Come here," you say.

He steps forward and you place your hand on his shoulder. "Return to the living." A surge of energy passes through your fingers.

Seconds later, Olderon blinks. He sees you and takes your hand. "My friend, you have saved me."

You smile. Then you turn to the multitude of undead creatures. "Return to what you were. Rest peacefully."

There is a great noise as a whirlwind of energy sweeps through the hall and out into the city. The undead begin to disappear. Ghouls vanish into the air, zombies decompose and banshees and skeletons crumble to dust. Then there is an explosion of light and you find yourself spinning in a whirlpool of energy.

When the light and noise subside, you are outside the Mountain of the Lost. The sun shines brightly, and Olderon and Hergal stand before you.

"You have succeeded in your quest," says Olderon. "What are you going to do with the Blood Crown?"

You think about the power you have...

If you wish to keep the Blood Crown for yourself, go to 26.

If you wish to give the crown to Olderon for safekeeping, go to 41.

5

You try to ignore the painful screeching of the banshees and string an arrow. You shoot at the creatures, but the arrow passes through their ghostly bodies.

The noise grows and you feel as though you could black out at any second.

To use the Ruby of Magic, go to 18.

If you wish to block up your ears, go to 31.

6

Once more you leap forward, swinging your sword, but every time you smash the skeleton, the bones simply re-form!

One of the skeleton's pikes catches the string holding the pouch containing the rubies. They spill on the ground. You grasp at them, but your enemy sees his chance. A blade slices through your arm and with a cry of pain, you drop your sword.

Immediately, the skeleton stabs at you with its six weapons. You drop to the ground, lifeless.

You've become a giant pincushion! To begin your adventure again, go to 1.

7

You guide Hergal towards the gap and find a place to land.

You take out the Ruby of Seeing to light your way. The gap in the mountain is too small for the gryphon to pass through. Leaving Hergal, you wade into the water and squeeze through the gap in the rock, into the mountain.

You head down a dark, narrow passage for some time; listening out for any enemies. The air gets colder and a shiver passes through your body.

Eventually you see an archway ahead. In the gloom, you make out the shapes of three troll-like creatures. Their low growls echo through the tunnel.

You move slowly towards the creatures. As you get closer to them, you nearly choke on the disgusting smell wafting through the passage! It is the smell of death.

If you wish to find out more about these creatures, go to 34.

If you wish to attack them, go to 3.

8

"I don't believe you," you say. You take out the Ruby of Seeing. A vision of a red marble palace appears and the word "north".

At that moment the soul-eater leaps at you, but you are ready for him. You smash him to the floor, where he lies unconscious. Placing the jar containing your soul inside your jacket, you head north.

You soon arrive at the Red Queen's palace. The entrance is guarded by a squad of fearsome zombie warriors. You march up to them.

"Take me to the Red Queen," you demand. "I have a message for her."

The captain of the guards steps forward. "And I have a message for you. Go away!"

You shake your head. "I'm here to stay."

"You asked for it then," he growls and swings at you with his spiked mace. It strikes your chest, but you still remain standing. "Nice try, but you cannot kill me," you say.

The zombies look amazed, but not for long as you take your sword and slice through them. You head into the palace and begin to hunt out the Red Queen and Mortha.

Go to 32.

9

You reach into the leather pouch containing the rubies and take out the Ruby of Power.

You urge Hergal towards the firebirds and pull out your bow and arrows. The ruby helps your aim and you strike home with several arrows, dropping your attackers through the sky like shooting stars.

But there are too many enemies to overcome. More firebirds join the attack. For every one you hit, another two appear, lighting up the sky with their flaming wings.

If you wish to retreat and find another way to the mountain, go to 44.

If you want to use the Ruby of Magic, go to 25.

10

You turn around and break out into a sprint across the narrow bridge, trying to get away from the warriors.

Before you can get very far, they are upon you, engulfing you in their unearthly bodies.

You try to beat them away with your sword, but the blade simply passes through their ghostly forms. As you thrash at your enemies, you lose your balance and fall from the bridge, plunging down onto the rocks far below.

You will never stop the Red Queen. To begin your quest again, go to 1.

"I am not here for talking," you say. With one swift movement you take out your bow, notch an arrow and shoot it at Mortha. It hits him in the middle of his chest.

There is a moment's pause and then Mortha smiles. He pulls out the arrow and it turns to ash in his hand. Before you can react he holds out his hand, sending a bolt of energy at you. It strikes you, lifting you into the air. You hang helplessly, unable to move as Mortha steps forward.

"So that is your answer. Very well." He reaches into your jacket and removes both the bag with the rubies in, and the jar containing your soul.

"Thank you for bringing us the rubies," he says. "You have made the whole process so much...easier." He throws the jar into the crowd of the undead. It breaks open, but before your soul can escape, the creatures leap on it. You cry out in pain and black out.

Go to 42.

12

You take out the Ruby of Seeing and a vision of Olderon forms in your mind. He is standing on the edge of a narrow gorge in the Mountain of the Lost.

Your former companion speaks. "Within this gorge is a secret entrance into the mountain. If you take any other way, you will surely die. You must take care though, your enemies are expecting you."

"How can I defeat them?" you ask.

"Death can never be defeated," replies Olderon. "You have to embrace it. To complete your quest you will have to give up your soul."

Before you can ask him what he means, the vision begins to fade. "We will meet again," Olderon says, and he vanishes.

Go to 49.

13

You drop your bow and with one movement pull your sword from its scabbard, swinging your blade at the draug's neck. You hit home and the creature's lifeless body drops to the floor.

You retrieve your arrows from the draugs'

bodies and make your way through the archway and onto a rocky ledge. You look down. Below you is the City of the Dead — Necropolis — home of the Red Queen!

You look around and see that there are two ways down to the city. To your left is a curving stone bridge that spans a chasm. To your right is a great waterfall. Next to this is a flight of steps carved out of the rock and leading down to the city.

If you wish to cross the bridge, go to 35.

If you would rather climb down the steps, go to 30.

14

You take out the Ruby of Seeing and ask it, "What should I do?"

Instead of receiving the answer to your question, a vision of Olderon appears in your head. You hear his words. "Death can never be defeated. You have to embrace it. You will have to give up your soul."

The vision vanishes and you wonder what to do next.

If you wish to search for the palace, go to 23.

If you want to ask for directions, go to 19.

15

You decide that an all-out attack on the entrance would be foolish. It is too well guarded. You steer Hergal away to look for another way into the mountain.

You fly along the black ridges of the mountain, searching the lower slopes. Eventually you see a stream emerging from a narrow gorge. You fly Hergal towards it and see that the stream is pouring out of a gap in the mountain. You realise that this could be the way into the City of the Dead!

Go to 7.

16

You know that you will not be able to fight your way to the crown, so you reach into your jacket, take out the jar and open it. Hundreds of souls fly out, including your own. Mortha and the Red Queen look puzzled.

Directed by your mind, your soul flies to the crown and settles on it...

You feel a great power surging through your body — you now have mastery over all of the rubies!

Mortha realises too late what you have done. He blasts you with an energy bolt, but it has no effect — the rubies have given you ultimate power!

Mortha flies at you. You take your sword and slice through his body. He disappears in a wisp of smoke...

"Attack him!" screams the Red Queen.

Go to 4.

17

You step through the white light and onto the bridge. As you do so you hear a rushing noise coming from behind you.

You spin around and see the light swirling in a whirlpool of colour. The light forms into a group of ghostly warriors, shimmering and sparkling in the darkness. They move towards you with their swords raised.

To fight these ghostly creatures, go to 24.

If you'd rather attempt to outrun them, go to 10.

18

You try to untie the leather pouch, but the screeching of the banshees has already taken hold of your mind. You cannot concentrate or focus. Your fingers are clumsy and too slow. Before you can take hold of the Ruby of Magic, the pain of the banshees' cries overcomes you. You black out and slump to the ground, leaving you at the mercy of the banshees.

To begin your quest again, go to 1.

You head towards the figure of a gnarly old man, sitting on a bench. He is staring into a glass jar, which seems to be filled with sparkling winged creatures that look like

golden moths.

Before you can say anything, the figure looks up. "Why are you here? You are not of this place..."

"I seek the palace of the Red Queen," you begin.

In the blink of an eye, the figure leaps up and places his hand against your chest. You suddenly feel weak, as if life is being sucked from your body. You drop to your knees. "What are you?" you gasp.

He points at the jar. "I am a collector of souls. Soon yours will be here with the others. Do not struggle, embrace your death and give your soul to me."

If you want to try to break free, go to 38.

If you decide to do what the soul collector says, go to 29.

20

As the draugs rush towards you they transform into giants. You smile at their stupidity — they have given you a bigger target to aim at!

You let your arrows fly and strike home. One

of the creatures drops down, groaning in pain. To your amazement, the other draugs laugh at his suffering. These creatures are stupid *and* cruel!

You dispatch another of the draugs with an arrow to its chest. The remaining giant charges towards you.

If you wish to continue to fight with your bow, go to 39.

If you wish to use your sword, go to 13.

21

You turn and look towards the marble building. As you do so, you feel a blow to the back of your head. You shouldn't have trusted the soul-eater!

You stagger forward, dropping the jar. It smashes on the ground, releasing the souls into the air. The collector begins to scoop them up in his hands.

You feel a great pressure in your chest — the collector has your soul!

"My mistress wishes to see you," he says, crushing your soul in his hand. You feel an intense pain in your chest, before you collapse, unconscious.

Go to 42.

22

You remember the vision of Olderon and the narrow gorge he was standing by.

You avoid flying near to the entrance and steer Hergal towards the east and the lower slopes of the mountain.

You soon see the narrow gorge and follow the stream that runs along it. You see that the stream is pouring out of a gap in the mountain. You realise that this is the way in!

Go to 7.

23

You continue to walk through the streets of Necropolis.

As you walk into a great square, you hear a shriek from above. You look up and see a swarm of death wraiths riding their firebirds heading for you.

Your enemies were expecting you...

The firebirds blaze towards you, swooping

down in a merciless attack. Before you can notch an arrow, a stream of blazing spears rains down on you. You try to avoid them, but it is impossible. One of the spears pierces your chest. You drop to the floor as more missiles rain down on your lifeless body.

So near, but so far! If you wish to begin again, go to 1.

24

You rush at the creatures, swinging your sword — but you simply pass through their ghostly bodies!

You step off the bridge and turn to face them, ready for a fight to the end. To your surprise, the warriors do not follow you. They stand with swords pointing at you.

You take out the Ruby of Seeing. "How do I pass these creatures?" you ask it.

The answer forms in your mind. *You cannot, for no living thing may cross the bridge.*

You will have to head for the waterfall.

Go to 30.

25

You reach into the leather pouch, pull out the Ruby of Magic and point it at your enemies. A bolt of energy erupts from the ruby, engulfing the firebirds.

You shield your eyes from the blazing inferno. The light dies away and you open your eyes. Nothing remains of the creatures.

Putting the ruby away, you stare into the distance. You can see swarms of wraiths and other nightmarish creatures flying towards the entrance into the mountain and the Red Queen's city.

If you wish to use the Ruby of Seeing, go to 12.

If you wish to continue flying towards the mountain, go to 49.

26

"I have tasted the power of the crown," you say. "I will keep it for myself. I will become all powerful!"

You laugh, but as you do so, you feel a great pain in your head. The rubies are burning into your skull. You try to tear the crown off your head, but you can't.

Olderon looks on in horror. "Why is this happening?" you cry.

The Ruby of Seeing reveals the answer — *Only a person of true honour can wear the crown.*

It is your last thought as the crown melts and you drop to the floor, dead.

Your greed has been your undoing. Try to rescue your honour by going back to 1.

27

You make your way to the gates. The skeleton guards point their weapons at you.

"Greetings," you begin, "I bring a message for your Queen."

One of the skeletons nods and points at the gate.

You smile. That was easy, you think. But as you step past the skeletons, you feel a ripping pain in your back.

You look down and see the point of a spear sticking out of your belly. You drop to your knees and pass into blackness.

Go to 42.

28

You take out the Ruby of Magic and the Ruby of Power, and speed towards the entrance.

The four-headed dogs detect you and begin

to howl. The trolls spot you and sound the alarm. You notch arrows and let fly, one after the other. The Ruby of Power guides your aim and you hit your target every time.

But to your horror, you see that the arrows are not killing your enemies.

The trolls unleash the dogs and they charge at you, their jaws dripping with poison. You suddenly realise why your enemies are not dying — they are already dead! You switch your attack to the Ruby of Magic. You blast the undead creatures into atoms, but this delay has cost you the element of surprise.

Hundreds of death wraiths, riding skeleton eagles, fly out of the entrance. The air is filled with missiles: spears and arrows, as hell is unleashed on you!

You try to escape, but Hergal is hit several times. Your faithful companion lets out a death cry and she plummets to the earth.

You hit the ground and the rubies fall from your grip.

Go to 40.

You recall Olderon's words about letting go of your soul and realise what you have to do. As the soul-eater pulls your soul from your body, you reach for the Ruby of Power.

The collector pulls a small ball of light from within your chest, opens the jar and places it carefully inside.

At that moment you snatch the jar from him and strike him. He falls to the ground, looking at you in amazement. "Why are you still standing?"

"Because of this." You show him the ruby. "It has given me a power beyond my own." You point at your soul in the jar. "Thanks to you, I am now the master of my soul. I am not fully alive, nor dead. As long as my soul is safe, outside my body, I cannot be killed. I think that will help me to defeat the Red Queen. Where is her palace?"

The soul-eater points towards a black marble building. "She is there..."

If you don't trust the soul-eater, go to 8.
If you do, go to 21.

You make your way to the steps and begin to climb down. The spray from the waterfall soaks you, but gives you cover from any prying eyes.

You continue downwards, treading carefully on the slippery rock steps.

Halfway down the cliff something seizes your ankle. You look down and see a tentacle wrapping itself around your leg. Before you can react you are pulled through the waterfall into a cave.

In the dim light you can just make out the outline of a creature from your worst nightmare. It is a devourer!

You are being pulled towards its open mouth, with its rows of razor-sharp teeth. Struggling for your life, you manage to pull your sword from its scabbard.

If you want to slash at the tentacle, go to 48.

If you want to wait until you get closer to the devourer's body, go to 2.

You rip two small pieces of cloth from your jacket and push them into your ears, blocking out the noise of the banshees.

You pull out the Ruby of Magic and destroy the fearsome creatures with a bolt of energy. In the blink of an eye they are reduced to dust. Your way to the Mountain of the Lost is clear! You remove the cloth from your ears and continue on your way.

If you used the Ruby of Seeing earlier, go to 22.

If you didn't, go to 47.

Inside the palace there are dozens of armed guards, but to your surprise they stand aside and let you pass.

Eventually you arrive at two blood-red wooden doors. You fling them open and enter a great hall. The hall is full of undead creatures of all forms, shapes and sizes.

At the far end of the hall sitting on two great thrones are Mortha and the Red Queen. In front of them is a black marble plinth. On it rests a

golden crown with a ruby set into the metal.
You realise that this is the Crown of Blood, and
the ruby is the Ruby of Death.

The Queen smiles. "Welcome, adventurer.
We have been expecting you!"

Mortha stands and holds out his hand. "You have brought the missing Blood Crown rubies to our city. So let me make you an offer for them…"

If you wish to attack Mortha, go to 11.
If you wish to listen to him, go to 45.

33

You know that the Ruby of Power will help you. You take out your sword and rush at the skeletons.

The guards are taken by surprise as you hack at their bones, instantly reducing three of them to splinters. The remaining guards fight back, stabbing at you with their pikes, but you avoid the blades and chop at their bones.

Soon all the skeletons lie in a pile.

You move towards the gate, but as you do so, you hear a scraping noise. You spin around to see the skeletons' bones moving and reattaching themselves together.

In seconds, the bones re-form into one giant, six-headed skeleton!

If you wish to fight the skeleton, go to 6.
To head through the gates, go to 43.

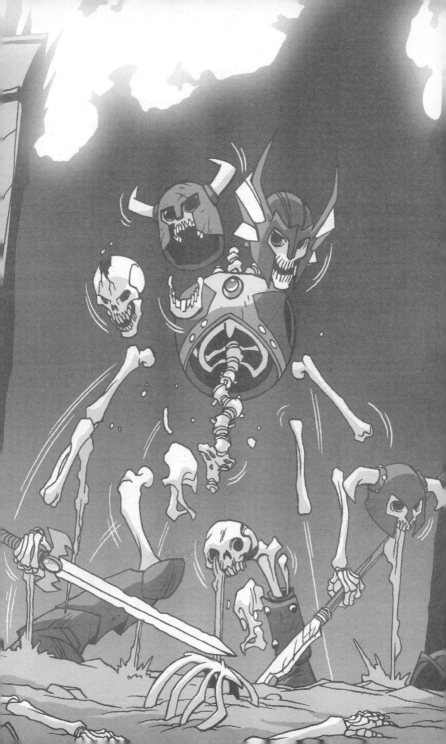

What are these beings, you wonder? The Ruby of Seeing gives you the answer. *These are draugs — undead creatures that can increase in size at will and possess unnatural strength. They delight in causing pain and suffering.*

The draugs spot you in the light cast by the Ruby of Seeing. They let out a great roar and move towards you. Their bodies fill the width of the passageway.

You decide to deal quickly with these creatures, and take out the Ruby of Magic. You point it at the draugs, but nothing happens. You wonder why. Again, the Ruby of Seeing gives you the answer. *Magic does not work in the land of the dead.*

What a great time to discover that, you think as the foul creatures get closer. You'll need to use a different tactic.

If you wish to attack quickly, go to 3.

If you want to use the Ruby of Power first, go to 46.

35

As you make your way towards the stone bridge, you see a transparent white light shimmering in the darkness. You grip your sword and move carefully forwards. A low murmuring of voices strikes up, but you can't see anyone or anything ahead of you.

If you wish to continue towards the bridge, go to 17.

To head back to the steps next to the waterfall, go to 30.

36

You decide that Mortha is right and you will never escape from Necropolis, but at least you and Olderon will live. It is with a heavy heart that you take the rubies from the pouch and hand them to the necromancer.

Smiling, he takes the rubies and puts them into the settings on the crown. Then he places the crown onto the Red Queen's head. She stands triumphant.

"And now you will allow us to leave?" you ask.

The Red Queen laughs. "Oh yes, but not as you are." She holds out her hand and from it shoots a stream of light. It hits you, dropping you to your knees.

"Olderon, do your duty."

Olderon steps forward. You are powerless to move as he takes the jar from your jacket. He opens it, takes out your soul and crushes it.

Your life has been taken from you! You are now one of the undead, another servant of the Red Queen.

You have failed at the last hurdle. To begin again, go to 1.

37

You pull at Hergal's reins as the deadly spears hurtle towards you. The gryphon twists and turns, but she cannot avoid all of the missiles. They pierce her side.

In desperation you reach for the leather pouch containing the Ruby of Magic, but you are too slow. The firebirds catch up with you and a skeleton leaps from the birds and attacks you. It knocks the pouch from your hands and the rubies fall into the valley far below.

You try to fight off the creature, but it is hopeless. Fire engulfs you as Hergal drops through the air. You let out a last scream that echoes round the Valley of the Demons. It is the last sound you will ever make.

You have failed in your quest. If you wish to begin again, go to 1.

38

You reach for your sword, but the collector takes a dagger from his belt and plunges it into your chest. You drop to the floor. A stream of sparkling light pours from the wound in your chest and shoots into the air.

The old man grasps at it, but cannot catch it. He curses. "One soul that that got away..."

He turns away, leaving your lifeless body on the floor.

You have failed. To begin again, go to 1.

39

As you shoot another arrow, the draug transforms into its original size. The arrow flies over its head. Before you can react, it leaps at you, knocking you to the ground.

The draug clutches at your throat and begins to tighten its grip. You struggle to break free and reach for the Ruby of Power, but the creature is too strong for you.

You feel the life being squeezed from your body. The draug howls in triumph as it slams your head against the rocky ground, and you pass thankfully into darkness.

To begin your quest again, go to 1.

40

Without the rubies, you are helpless. Your enemies close in on you. You try to fight back, but you are soon overwhelmed.

Your flesh is pierced time and again, and your lifeblood pours from your body.

If you wish to begin your quest again, go to 1.

41

You touch the crown and think that you could become what the Red Queen wanted to be — ruler of the world!

Then you shake your head. "The temptation is great," you say. "But I do not wish for such power. I said I would return the crown, and so I will. In the meantime, you take care of it. I have felt its power and do not wish to be tempted again."

You hand the crown to Olderon, who places it in Hergal's saddlebag.

Olderon turns to you. "You have chosen wisely," he says.

You smile.

"It is time to return home," you say.

Go to 50.

42

After some time, you regain consciousness. You are standing in the hall of the Red Queen.

She and her husband Mortha sit in their thrones. "Bow before me," demands the Queen.

You fall to your knees. "Yes, Mistress," you reply, "I am your servant, now and forever!"

You have become one of the undead! If you wish to begin your quest again, go to 1.

43

You realise that there is no way to destroy this creature, so you sprint for the gate. The skeleton follows, but you are too quick for it. You pass through the gate and slam it shut.

You begin to make your way through the city, passing beings including zombies, skeletons and wraiths — every one is undead! They stare at you, but allow you to go on your way. You think this is strange, but are glad you don't have to fight all of them. You know that you have to find the Red Queen's palace and the Ruby of Death.

If you wish to use the Ruby of Seeing, go to 14.

If you wish to try to communicate with one of the undead beings, go to 19.

44

You turn Hergal around and try to outfly the firebirds. However, the creatures are too fast. One of them draws level with you. You glance across and see the skeleton rider drawing back his arm and hurling a flaming spear at you. It misses you, but it strikes Hergal's wing.

The gryphon gives a shriek of pain as her feathers catch alight. You pull the burning spear from her wing and beat at the flames, putting them out. More firebirds close in and their riders hurl their deadly missiles towards you.

If you want to use the Ruby of Magic, go to 25.

If you wish to try to dodge the spears, go to 37.

45

"I am listening," you say.

Mortha steps forward. "We have been following your adventures. You have impressed us with your skill and bravery, but now you are here you have no chance of escape."

"So you say," you reply.

Mortha shakes his head. "You are brave, but foolish if you think you can defeat us here in our city."

"I will die trying," you say.

Mortha laughs. "But we do not wish to kill you! We wish to make you an offer." He clicks his fingers and from out of the shadows steps a familiar figure.

"Olderon!" you cry.

A death wraith stands at his side, gloating. You realise that Olderon is now one of the Red Queen's undead followers!

Mortha smiles. "This is what we propose. Give us the rubies and we will give life back to your companion, and you can leave. If not, we will take them anyway. What do you say?"

Olderon stares at you as you decide what you should do.

If you wish to attack Mortha, go to 11.

If you wish to give up the rubies, go to 36.

If you want to try to take the Blood Crown, go to 16.

46

You reach into your pouch and grasp the Ruby of Power. You feel the warmth of its strength surge through your body.

One of the draugs sniffs and grunts at the air as it closes in on you. "I smell live flesh!" it roars.

Before the draugs get too close, you quickly draw your bow and notch an arrow.

Go to 20.

47

As you get nearer to the mountain, you see that the entrance leading into the City of the Dead is guarded by dozens of armed zombie trolls. Their rotting flesh hangs off their bodies. Giant dogs with four heads stalk around, sniffing at the air and letting out howls that echo through the valley.

Smoke and fire pour from the entrance and the stench of death is all around. This is a truly terrifying place.

If you wish to try to fight your way into the mountain, go to 28.

If you wish to look for another way into the mountain, go to 15.

48

In desperation, you slash at the tentacle with your sword as the creature pulls you towards its mouth, and certain death.

Time and time again you hack at the devourer's flesh. Finally, the blade slices through and the tentacle drops twitching to the floor. A stream of green blood oozes out from the wound. The devourer lets out a

demonic scream.

You scramble at the slippery rock, trying to escape, but before you can get away another tentacle flicks out, catching your hand.
Your sword is sent spinning from your grip.
It clatters to the ground out of reach. More tentacles grab hold of your arms and legs, and wrap you up. You cannot move!

You try to break free from the creature's grip as it pulls you towards its open mouth. But your struggles are in vain. It gives a roar of triumph. You scream as its teeth crunch down on you.

The devourer lived up to its name! To begin again, go to 1.

49

You steer Hergal towards the Mountain of the Lost.

As you get nearer, the valley suddenly fills with the sound of demonic screeching. You try to block out the noise, but it is impossible.

The air is filled with flying ghost-like shapes — they are flesh-eating screaming banshees! You have heard of these creatures. Their deadly screeching sends their victims into

unconsciousness before the banshees rip them apart.

The creatures fly around you. Hergal seems not to be affected by them, but your head feels as though it is splitting apart. Your eardrums throb to bursting point.

To fight the creatures, go to 5.

To use the Ruby of Magic, go to 18.

If you wish to block up your ears, go to 31.

50

Hergal flies you and Olderon back to Alba where you receive a hero's welcome.

In the great hall, you tell the Queen of Alba and her councillors of your many adventures since you left the court.

When you have finished your story, you hand over the Blood Crown. The queen takes it and thanks you.

"We will keep this and it will once again be a force for good," she says. "You will be its guardian, for you have proved yourself brave, strong and worthy."

You are a true hero!

You are a member of a Special Forces military unit. You have flown many secret military planes, and even tested prototype space vehicles and advanced weapons. You are the top-ranking test pilot in the force.

After your latest Special Forces mission, you are taking some well-earned rest. You are relaxing at home, watching a news bulletin. There are reports of strange weather patterns across the world. Typhoons, hurricanes, thunderstorms and sandstorms are battering cities, causing death and destruction across the planet.

At that moment your doorbell rings. You open the door to reveal a man and a woman, both dressed in stiff black suits. They show you their IDs.

"Agent Roberts," the man says, "and this is Agent Lee. We're with Earth Defence."

"Never heard of it," you say.

"That's because it's a top-secret unit," replies Roberts.

"We need your help," says Lee.

CONTINUE READING IN TYRANNO QUEST
AIR BLAST

Decide the fate
of the Earth with
these four Tyranno
Quest titles!

978 1 4451 0875 9 pb   978 1 4451 1345 6 eBook

978 1 4451 0876 6 pb   978 1 4451 1346 3 eBook

978 1 4451 0877 3 pb   978 1 4451 1347 0 eBook

978 1 4451 0878 0 pb   978 1 4451 1348 7 eBook

About the 2Steves

"The 2Steves" are
Britain's most popular
writing double act
for young people,
specialising in comedy
and adventure. They
perform regularly in schools and libraries,
and at festivals, taking the power of words
and story to audiences of all ages.

Together they have written many books,
including the *Crime Team* and *iHorror* series.

About the illustrator: Jack Lawrence

Jack Lawrence is a successful freelance
comics illustrator, working on titles such as
A.T.O.M., Cartoon Network, *Doctor Who
Adventures*, *2000 AD*, *Gogos Mega Metropolis*
and *Spider-Man Tower of Power*. He also works
as a freelance toy designer.

Jack lives in Maidstone in Kent with
his partner and two cats.

Want to read more "You Are The Hero" adventures? Well, why not try these...

Also by the 2Steves: iHorror
Fight your fear. Choose your fate.

978 1 40830 985 8 pb
978 1 40831 476 0 eBook

978 1 40830 986 5 pb
978 1 40831 477 7 eBook

978 1 40830 988 9 pb
978 1 40831 479 1 eBook

978 1 40830 987 2 pb
978 1 40831 478 4 eBook

How to be a hero

This book is not like others you may have read. You are the hero of this adventure. It is up to you to make decisions that will affect how the adventure unfolds.

Each section of this book is numbered. At the end of most sections, you will have to make a choice. The choice you make will take you to a different section of the book.

Some of your choices will help you to complete the adventure successfully. But choose carefully, some of your decisions could be fatal!

If you fail, then start the adventure again and learn from your mistake.

If you choose correctly you will succeed in your mission.

Don't be a zero, be a hero!

The quest so far...

You are a skilled warrior, living in a world of enchantment and danger. Humans live alongside trolls, elves and dwarves, while other mysterious creatures walk in the shadows.

The Queen of Alba has asked for your help against her deadliest foes — the Red Queen and her husband, Mortha, the necromancer.

Many years ago Solmor, the world's greatest Spellcaster, created a crown of gold set with four great rubies. The Ruby of Power gave its owner fighting skills. The Ruby of Seeing, the gift of telepathy and reading minds. The Ruby of Magic, powers of enchantment. The Ruby of Death, mastery over the world of the dead.

But rulers across the world wanted the power of the Crown of Rubies for themselves. It became a force for evil and was renamed the Blood Crown.

Just before his death, Solmor destroyed the crown and had the rubies hidden across the globe, so no one could find them.

Now the Red Queen and her necromancer husband are hunting for them. They already possess the Ruby of Death. If they succeed in finding the others, your world will be plunged into a new dark age. They have already killed your friend Olderon.

But you possess the Ruby of Power, the Ruby of Seeing and the Ruby of Magic. All you need now is the Ruby of Death, and your quest will be complete.

You are now on your gryphon, Hergal, flying to Necropolis — the City of the Dead. There you will have to use the rubies you have found to defeat the Red Queen and Mortha, and take the Ruby of Death from them. If you do not, and they take the last three rubies, then the world will fall under their control and all will be lost...

Go to 1.

1

The Ruby of Magic has revealed to you the location of Necropolis, the City of the Dead. It lies in the depths of the earth under the Mountain of the Lost.

After days of travelling on Hergal, you fly into the Valley of the Demons.

Ahead you can see the Mountain of the Lost, spewing out fire into the black night sky. The strong smell of sulphur chokes the air. This is a place of nightmares!

Suddenly dozens of firebirds appear from out of the stinking clouds. They are being ridden by skeletons armed with flaming spears. You have met these creatures before, and know how deadly they are!

If you wish to fight the creatures, go to 9.

If you wish to find another way to the mountain, go to 44.

You wait, your sword held high, as the devourer pulls you nearer to its mouth. When you are close enough to its head, you grasp your sword with both hands and plunge it down into the beast's head.

The devourer lets out a screech that echoes around the cave, and finally lets go of your leg. You leap up and stab the creature again. Within seconds, the devourer's tentacles flop down onto the rock and the huge beast lies dead at your feet.

You carefully step through the waterfall and back onto the rocky steps.

Soon you are at the bottom of the cliff and heading towards Necropolis. Ahead of you are the gates to the city. You see that they're guarded by half a dozen heavily armed skeletons.

If you wish to fight your way into the city, go to 33.

If you wish to try to talk your way into the city, go to 27.